Complete Zero Point Cooking for two Recipes

Effortless and Flavorful Cooking for Two, Designed to Help You Shed Pounds and Achieve Your Weight Loss Goals.

DR. HELENA M. OLIVIA

Copyright Page

TABLE OF CONTENTS

CONCEPT OF ZERO POINT FOODS

Zero Point Foods are foods that have a low or zero SmartPoints value in certain diet programs. These programs assign points to different foods based on their nutritional content. The idea behind Zero Point Foods is that you can enjoy these foods without having to count their points towards your daily allowance. The specific Zero Point Foods can vary depending on the diet program you're following. Usually, these foods are low in calories and high in nutrients, like fruits, vegetables, lean proteins, and whole grains. Since they are lower in calories, you can eat them in larger quantities without worrying about going over your daily points. Including Zero Point Foods in your meals and snacks can help you feel satisfied while staying on track with your goals. They provide a great opportunity to make healthier choices and incorporate more nutritious options into your diet.

- **Weight Loss Programs:** Zero point foods are commonly featured in weight loss programs that utilize a points-based system to help individuals track their food intake. These programs assign points to different foods based on their nutritional content, with the goal of encouraging healthier eating habits and portion control.

- **Zero Point Value:** Foods designated as zero point foods are given a point value of zero, meaning individuals can consume them without counting them towards their daily point allowance. This encourages the consumption of these foods as part of a balanced diet.

- **Nutrient Density:** Zero point foods are typically nutrient-dense, meaning they provide a high amount of nutrients relative to their calorie content. These foods often include fruits, vegetables, lean proteins, and certain whole grains. By focusing on these foods, individuals can increase their intake of essential vitamins, minerals, and fiber while keeping their calorie intake in check.

- **Portion Control:** While zero point foods may be assigned zero points, portion control is still important. Consuming excessive amounts of these foods can still contribute to weight gain. Weight loss programs often provide guidance on portion sizes to help individuals make informed choices about their food intake.

- **Flexibility:** Zero point foods offer flexibility within the program, allowing individuals to build meals and snacks around these foods without feeling restricted. This flexibility can help individuals adhere to their dietary goals over the long term and maintain a balanced and sustainable approach to eating.

BENEFITS OF ZERO POINT FOODS FOR WEIGHT LOSS

- **Low in Calories:** Zero point foods are typically low in calories, which means you can consume them in larger quantities without significantly increasing your overall calorie intake. This can help you feel satisfied and full while still adhering to a calorie deficit, which is necessary for weight loss.

- **High in Nutrients:** Despite being low in calories, zero point foods are often rich in essential nutrients such as vitamins, minerals, and antioxidants. Consuming a variety of nutrient-dense foods supports overall health and well-being, ensuring you get the necessary nutrients while cutting calories for weight loss.

- **Promotes Satiety:** Many zero point foods are high in fiber, water, and protein, all of which contribute to feelings of fullness and satiety. By incorporating these foods into your meals, you can help control hunger and cravings, making it easier to stick to your weight loss plan without feeling deprived.

- **Encourages Healthy Eating Habits:** By focusing on these foods, you naturally reduce your intake of less healthy options like processed foods, sugary snacks, and high-fat foods, promoting a healthier overall diet.

- **Flexibility and Variety:** Zero point foods offer flexibility in meal planning and allow for a wide variety of food choices. This can help prevent boredom with your diet and make it easier to stick to your weight loss goals in the long term.

- **Supports Sustainable Weight Loss:** Because zero point foods are nutritious, filling, and satisfying, they support sustainable weight loss by providing a foundation for a balanced and enjoyable eating plan.

- **Blood Sugar Control:** Foods like non-starchy vegetables and lean proteins have minimal impact on blood sugar levels, which is beneficial for individuals with diabetes or those looking to stabilize their blood sugar levels.

GRILLED LEMON GARLIC SHRIMP SKEWERS

 Prep Time
10 Mins

Cook Time
8 Mins

Yields
2 Servings

Marinating Time: 30 Mins

INGREDIENTS

- 12 large shrimp, peeled and deveined
- 2 cloves garlic, minced
- 1 lemon, zest and juice
- 1 tablespoon fresh parsley, chopped
- Salt and pepper to taste
- Wooden or metal skewers (if using wooden skewers, soak them in water for 30 minutes before using)

DIRECTIONS

- In a small bowl, combine the minced garlic, lemon zest, lemon juice, chopped parsley, salt, and pepper to make the marinade.
- Thread the shrimp onto skewers, dividing evenly between the two skewers.
- Place the shrimp skewers in a shallow dish and pour the marinade over them, ensuring they are well coated. Let them marinate for 15-30 minutes in the refrigerator.
- Preheat the grill to medium-high heat.

8

NUTRITIONAL FACTS (PER SERVING)

- Calories: 80kcal
- Total Fat: 1g
- Saturated Fat: 0g
- Cholesterol: 90mg
- Sodium: 230mg
- Carbohydrates: 4g
- Dietary Fiber: 1g
- Sugars: 0g
- Protein: 15g

DIRECTIONS

- Once the grill is hot, place the shrimp skewers on the grill and cook for 2-3 minutes per side, or until the shrimp are pink and opaque.
- Remove the shrimp skewers from the grill and serve immediately.

CUCUMBER AVOCADO GAZPACHO

Prep Time
10 Mins

Chill Time
1 Hr

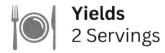

Yields
2 Servings

INGREDIENTS

- 1 large cucumber, peeled and chopped
- 1 ripe avocado, peeled and pitted
- 1 cup plain non-fat Greek yogurt
- 1 clove garlic, minced
- 2 tablespoons fresh lemon juice
- 2 tablespoons fresh cilantro, chopped
- Salt and pepper to taste
- Optional garnish: diced cucumber, avocado slices, and cilantro leaves.

DIRECTIONS

- In a blender or food processor, combine the chopped cucumber, avocado, Greek yogurt, minced garlic, lemon juice, and chopped cilantro.
- Blend the ingredients until smooth and creamy.
- Season the gazpacho with salt and pepper to taste. Adjust the seasoning according to your preference.
- Transfer the gazpacho to a bowl or container and refrigerate for at least 1 hour to chill and allow the flavors to meld.
- Once chilled, divide the gazpacho into two bowls for serving.
- Garnish each bowl with diced cucumber,

NUTRITIONAL FACTS (PER SERVING)

- Calories: 150kcal
- Total Fat: 9g
- Saturated Fat: 1g
- Cholesterol: 0mg
- Sodium: 50mg
- Carbohydrates: 14g
- Dietary Fiber: 7g
- Sugars: 4g
- Protein: 9g

DIRECTIONS

- avocado slices, and cilantro leaves if desired.

SEARED TUNA SALAD WITH CITRUS VINAIGRETTE

 Prep Time
10 Mins

Cook Time
6 Mins

 Yields
2 Servings

INGREDIENTS

For the Salad:
- 2 tuna steaks (about 4-6 ounces each)
- 6 cups mixed salad greens
- 1 cup cherry tomatoes, halved
- 1/2 cucumber, sliced
- 1/4 red onion, thinly sliced
- Salt and pepper to taste
- Cooking spray or olive oil for searing

For the Citrus Vinaigrette:
- 2 tablespoons fresh lemon juice
- 2 tablespoons fresh orange juice
- 1 tablespoon olive oil
- 1 teaspoon Dijon mustard
- 1 teaspoon honey (optional)
- Salt and pepper to taste

DIRECTIONS

- In a small bowl, whisk together the lemon juice, orange juice, olive oil, Dijon mustard, honey (if using), salt, and pepper to make the citrus vinaigrette. Set aside.
- Season the tuna steaks with salt and pepper on both sides.
- Heat a non-stick skillet or grill pan over medium-high heat. Lightly coat the pan with cooking spray or a drizzle of olive oil.
- Once the pan is hot, add the tuna steaks and sear for 1-2 minutes on each side, or until desired doneness. For medium-rare, aim for a slightly pink center.

NUTRITIONAL FACTS (PER SERVING)

- Calories: 250kcal
- Total Fat: 10g
- Saturated Fat: 1.5g
- Cholesterol: 55mg
- Sodium: 150mg
- Carbohydrates: 11g
- Dietary Fiber: 3g
- Sugars: 6g
- Protein: 30g

DIRECTIONS

- While the tuna is cooking, divide the mixed salad greens between two plates. Top with cherry tomatoes, cucumber slices, and red onion.
- Once the tuna is cooked to your liking, remove it from the heat and let it rest for a minute.
- Slice the tuna steaks thinly and arrange them on top of the prepared salads.
- Drizzle the citrus vinaigrette over the salads just before serving.

STUFFED PORTOBELLO MUSHROOMS

 Prep Time
15 Mins

Cook Time
20 Mins

 Yields
2 Servings

INGREDIENTS

- 2 large Portobello mushrooms
- 1 cup diced vegetables (such as bell peppers, onions, zucchini, etc.)
- 2 cloves garlic, minced
- 1/2 cup chopped fresh spinach
- 1/4 cup marinara sauce (look for a low-sugar or sugar-free option to keep it zero points)
- Salt and pepper to taste
- Cooking spray
- Optional toppings: grated Parmesan cheese, fresh herbs

DIRECTIONS

- Preheat your oven to 375°F (190°C).
- Clean the Portobello mushrooms by gently wiping them with a damp cloth. Remove the stems and scoop out the gills using a spoon. Set aside.
- In a skillet, heat cooking spray over medium heat. Add diced vegetables and minced garlic. Cook until vegetables are tender, about 5-7 minutes.
- Stir in chopped spinach and cook until wilted. Season with salt and pepper to taste.
- Remove the skillet from heat and stir in marinara sauce.
- Place the Portobello mushrooms on a baking sheet lined with

NUTRITIONAL FACTS (PER SERVING)

- Calories: 50kcal
- Total Fat: 0.5g
- Saturated Fat: 0g
- Cholesterol: 0mg
- Sodium: 130mg
- Carbohydrates: 10g
- Dietary Fiber: 3g
- Sugars: 5g
- Protein: 4g

DIRECTIONS

- parchment paper or aluminum foil, gill side up.
- Divide the vegetable mixture evenly and stuff it into the Portobello mushrooms.
- Bake in the preheated oven for 15-20 minutes, or until the mushrooms are tender.
- Once cooked, you can optionally sprinkle grated Parmesan cheese or fresh herbs on top before serving.

BAKED SALMON WITH DILL AND LEMON

 Prep Time
5 Mins

Cook Time
15 Mins

 **Yields**
2 Servings

INGREDIENTS

- 2 salmon fillets (about 4-6 ounces each)
- 1 tablespoon fresh dill, chopped
- 1 lemon, thinly sliced
- Salt and pepper, to taste
- Cooking spray or olive oil spray

DIRECTIONS

- Preheat your oven to 375°F (190°C).
- Line a baking sheet with parchment paper or lightly grease it with cooking spray.
- Place the salmon fillets on the prepared baking sheet.
- Season the salmon with salt, pepper, and chopped dill.
- Top each salmon fillet with lemon slices.
- Bake in the preheated oven for 12-15 minutes, or until the salmon is cooked through and flakes easily with a fork.
- Once done, remove from the oven and serve immediately.

NUTRITIONAL FACTS (PER SERVING)

- Calories: 220kcal
- Total Fat: 10g
- Saturated Fat: 2g
- Cholesterol: 80mg
- Sodium: 80mg
- Carbohydrates: 3g
- Dietary Fiber: 1g
- Sugars: 1g
- Protein: 30g

LENTIL SPROUT SALAD

 Prep Time
10 Mins

Cook Time
0 Mins

 **Yields**
2 Servings

INGREDIENTS

- 1 cup lentil sprouts
- 1 cup mixed greens (such as spinach, arugula, or lettuce)
- 1/2 cup cherry tomatoes, halved
- 1/4 cup diced cucumber
- 1/4 cup diced bell pepper (any color)
- 1/4 cup diced red onion
- 1 tablespoon chopped fresh herbs (such as parsley, cilantro, or mint)
- Juice of 1 lemon
- Salt and pepper to taste.

DIRECTIONS

- In a large bowl, combine the lentil sprouts, mixed greens, cherry tomatoes, cucumber, bell pepper, red onion, and fresh herbs.
- Squeeze the lemon juice over the salad and toss gently to combine.
- Season with salt and pepper to taste.
- Serve immediately or refrigerate until ready to serve.

NUTRITIONAL FACTS (PER SERVING)

- Calories: 70kcal
- Total Fat: 0.5g
- Saturated Fat: 0g
- Cholesterol: 0mg
- Sodium: 10mg
- Carbohydrates: 14g
- Dietary Fiber: 4g
- Sugars: 2g
- Protein: 4g

GREEK YOGURT CHICKEN SALAD

 Prep Time
10 Mins

Cook Time
15 Mins

 **Yields**
2 Servings

Fermentation Time: 3 Days

INGREDIENTS

- 2 boneless, skinless chicken breasts (about 8 oz each)
- 1/2 cup non-fat Greek yogurt
- 1 tablespoon lemon juice
- 1 tablespoon Dijon mustard
- 1/4 cup diced celery
- 1/4 cup diced red onion
- 1/4 cup diced cucumber
- Salt and pepper to taste
- Optional: fresh herbs such as parsley or dill for garnish

DIRECTIONS

- Season the chicken breasts with salt and pepper on both sides.
- Heat a non-stick skillet over medium heat. Cook the chicken breasts for 6-8 minutes per side, or until cooked through and no longer pink in the center. Remove from heat and let cool.
- Once the chicken is cool enough to handle, dice it into small pieces and transfer to a mixing bowl.
- In the same bowl, add Greek yogurt, lemon juice, and Dijon mustard. Mix until well combined.
- Add diced celery, red onion, and cucumber to the bowl with the

NUTRITIONAL FACTS (PER SERVING)

- Calories: 220kcal
- Total Fat: 3g
- Saturated Fat: 0.5g
- Cholesterol: 90mg
- Sodium: 270mg
- Carbohydrates: 5g
- Dietary Fiber: 1g
- Sugars: 3g
- Protein: 40g

DIRECTIONS

- chicken mixture. Stir until everything is evenly coated.
- Taste and adjust seasoning with salt and pepper if needed.
- Garnish with fresh herbs if desired.
- Serve immediately or refrigerate until ready to serve.

MEDITERRANEAN QUINOA SALAD

 Prep Time 10 Mins   **Cook Time** 15 Mins    **Yields** 2 Servings

INGREDIENTS

- 1/2 cup uncooked quinoa
- 1 cup water
- 1 cup cherry tomatoes, halved
- 1/2 cucumber, diced
- 1/4 cup red onion, finely chopped
- 1/4 cup Kalamata olives, pitted and sliced
- 1/4 cup crumbled feta cheese (optional)
- 2 tbsp fresh lemon juice
- 2 tbsp extra virgin olive oil
- 1 garlic clove, minced
- 1/2 tsp dried oregano
- Salt and pepper to taste
- Fresh parsley for garnish (optional)

DIRECTIONS

- Rinse the quinoa under cold water. In a small saucepan, combine the quinoa and water. Bring to a boil, then reduce the heat to low, cover, and simmer for 15 minutes, or until the quinoa is cooked and the water is absorbed. Remove from heat and let it cool.
- In a large mixing bowl, combine the cooked quinoa, cherry tomatoes, cucumber, red onion, and Kalamata olives.
- In a small bowl, whisk together the lemon juice, olive oil, minced garlic, dried oregano, salt, and pepper to make the dressing.

NUTRITIONAL FACTS (PER SERVING)

- Calories: 242kcal
- Total Fat: 12g
- Saturated Fat: 1.6g
- Cholesterol: 0mg
- Sodium: 10mg
- Carbohydrates: 30g
- Dietary Fiber: 4g
- Sugars: 3g
- Protein: 5g

DIRECTIONS

- Pour the dressing over the quinoa salad and toss to coat all the ingredients evenly.
- If using, sprinkle the crumbled feta cheese over the salad and gently toss again.
- Taste and adjust seasoning if needed.
- Garnish with fresh parsley if desired.
- Serve immediately or chill in the refrigerator for at least 30 minutes before serving to allow the flavors to meld.

CAULIFLOWER FRIED RICE

 Prep Time
10 Mins

Cook Time
15 Mins

 **Yields**
2 Servings

INGREDIENTS

- 1 small head of cauliflower, riced (about 3 cups)
- 1 tablespoon low-sodium soy sauce (or tamari for gluten-free option)
- 1 tablespoon sesame oil
- 2 cloves garlic, minced
- 1/2 cup diced onion
- 1/2 cup diced carrots
- 1/2 cup diced bell pepper (any color)
- 1/2 cup frozen peas
- 2 eggs, beaten
- Salt and pepper to taste
- Optional toppings: sliced green onions, sesame seeds, sriracha

DIRECTIONS

- Prepare the cauliflower rice by either grating the cauliflower florets using a box grater or pulsing them in a food processor until they resemble rice grains.
- In a small bowl, mix the soy sauce and sesame oil together. Set aside.
- Heat a large skillet or wok over medium-high heat. Add the minced garlic and diced onion, and sauté until fragrant and translucent, about 2-3 minutes.
- Add the diced carrots and bell pepper to the skillet. Cook for another 3-4 minutes, or until the vegetables are tender.
- Push the vegetables to one side of the skillet and

NUTRITIONAL FACTS (PER SERVING)

- Calories: 140kcal
- Total Fat: 7g
- Saturated Fat: 1g
- Cholesterol: 186mg
- Sodium: 330mg
- Carbohydrates: 14g
- Dietary Fiber: 5g
- Sugars: 6g
- Protein: 9g

DIRECTIONS

- pour the beaten eggs into the empty space. Allow the eggs to cook undisturbed for a minute or two, then scramble them using a spatula until cooked through.
- Add the cauliflower rice and frozen peas to the skillet. Pour the soy sauce mixture over the rice and mix well to combine all ingredients.
- Cook for an additional 5-7 minutes, stirring frequently, until the cauliflower rice is tender and heated through.
- Season with salt and pepper to taste. Serve hot, garnished with sliced green onions, sesame seeds, and a drizzle of sriracha if desired.

CAPRESE STUFFED CHICKEN BREAST

 Prep Time
15 Mins

Cook Time
30 Mins

 Yields
2 Servings

INGREDIENTS

- 2 boneless, skinless chicken breasts
- 1 large tomato, thinly sliced
- 4 slices of fresh mozzarella cheese
- 1/4 cup fresh basil leaves
- Salt and pepper, to taste
- Olive oil spray or 1 teaspoon olive oil

DIRECTIONS

- Preheat your oven to 375°F (190°C).
- Butterfly each chicken breast by slicing horizontally through the middle, but not all the way through, so you can open it like a book.
- Season the inside of each chicken breast with salt and pepper.
- Layer the inside of each chicken breast with tomato slices, fresh basil leaves, and mozzarella cheese slices.
- Close the chicken breasts over the stuffing, securing with toothpicks if necessary.
- Lightly spray a baking dish with olive oil spray or brush with olive oil to prevent sticking.

NUTRITIONAL FACTS (PER SERVING)

- Calories: 270kcal
- Total Fat: 12g
- Saturated Fat: 6g
- Cholesterol: 102mg
- Sodium: 250mg
- Carbohydrates: 3g
- Dietary Fiber: 1g
- Sugars: 2g
- Protein: 36g

DIRECTIONS

- Place the stuffed chicken breasts in the baking dish.
- Season the top of each chicken breast with a little more salt and pepper.
- Bake in the preheated oven for 25-30 minutes, or until the chicken is cooked through and no longer pink in the center.
- Once cooked, remove the toothpicks before serving.
- Serve hot, garnished with additional fresh basil if desired.

VEGETABLE AND BEAN SOUP

 Prep Time
15 Mins

Cook Time
25 Mins

 Yields
4 Servings

INGREDIENTS

- 2 cups low-sodium vegetable broth
- 1 can (15 oz) diced tomatoes, undrained
- 1 cup chopped carrots
- 1 cup chopped celery
- 1 cup chopped onion
- 1 cup chopped bell peppers (any color)
- 2 cloves garlic, minced
- 1 teaspoon dried thyme
- 1 teaspoon dried oregano
- 1/2 teaspoon smoked paprika
- 1/4 teaspoon black pepper
- 1 can (15 oz) kidney beans, drained and rinsed
- 1 can (15 oz) chickpeas (garbanzo beans), drained and rinsed
- 2 cups chopped spinach or kale
- Salt to taste

DIRECTIONS

- In a large pot, combine the vegetable broth, diced tomatoes, carrots, celery, onion, bell peppers, garlic, thyme, oregano, smoked paprika, and black pepper. Bring to a simmer over medium heat.
- Once simmering, reduce the heat to low and let the soup cook for about 15-20 minutes, or until the vegetables are tender.
- Stir in the kidney beans, chickpeas, and chopped spinach or kale. Cook for an additional 5 minutes until the beans are heated through and the greens are wilted.
- Taste the soup and adjust seasoning with salt as needed.

NUTRITIONAL FACTS (PER SERVING)

- Calories: 190kcal
- Total Fat: 1g
- Saturated Fat: 0g
- Cholesterol: 0mg
- Sodium: 350mg
- Carbohydrates: 38g
- Dietary Fiber: 10g
- Sugars: 9g
- Protein: 10g

DIRECTIONS

- Ladle the soup into bowls and garnish with fresh herbs if desired.

BROCCOLI AND CHEDDAR STUFFED CHICKEN BREAST

 Prep Time
10 Mins

Cook Time
30 Mins

 Yields
2 Servings

INGREDIENTS

- 2 boneless, skinless chicken breasts
- 1 cup steamed broccoli florets, chopped
- 1/4 cup shredded reduced-fat cheddar cheese
- 1/2 teaspoon garlic powder
- 1/2 teaspoon onion powder
- Salt and pepper to taste
- Cooking spray

DIRECTIONS

- Preheat your oven to 375°F (190°C).
- Place each chicken breast between two sheets of plastic wrap or parchment paper and pound them to an even thickness using a meat mallet or rolling pin.
- In a small mixing bowl, combine the chopped broccoli, shredded cheddar cheese, garlic powder, onion powder, salt, and pepper.
- Divide the broccoli and cheese mixture evenly between the chicken breasts, spreading it over one half of each breast.
- Fold the other half of each chicken breast over the filling, pressing the edges to seal.

30

NUTRITIONAL FACTS (PER SERVING)

- Calories: 225kcal
- Total Fat: 6g
- Saturated Fat: 2g
- Cholesterol: 90mg
- Sodium: 235mg
- Carbohydrates: 4g
- Dietary Fiber: 2g
- Sugars: 1g
- Protein: 38g

DIRECTIONS

- Place the stuffed chicken breasts on a baking sheet lined with parchment paper or coated with cooking spray.
- Lightly spray the tops of the chicken breasts with cooking spray and season with additional salt and pepper if desired.
- Bake in the preheated oven for 25-30 minutes, or until the chicken is cooked through and the internal temperature reaches 165°F (74°C).

SMOKY CHICKPEA AND EGGPLANT STEW

 Prep Time
10 Mins

Cook Time
25 Mins

 Yields
4 Servings

INGREDIENTS

- 1 small eggplant, diced
- 1 can (15 oz) chickpeas, drained and rinsed
- 1 onion, diced
- 2 cloves garlic, minced
- 1 red bell pepper, diced
- 1 can (14.5 oz) diced tomatoes
- 2 cups vegetable broth
- 1 tsp smoked paprika
- 1/2 tsp cumin
- Salt and pepper to taste
- Fresh parsley or cilantro for garnish (optional)
- Cooking spray or olive oil for sautéing

DIRECTIONS

- Heat a large pot or Dutch oven over medium heat. Lightly coat the bottom with cooking spray or olive oil.
- Add the diced onion and minced garlic to the pot, sautéing until softened and fragrant, about 2-3 minutes.
- Add the diced eggplant and red bell pepper to the pot. Cook for another 5 minutes, stirring occasionally, until vegetables begin to soften.
- Stir in the smoked paprika and cumin, coating the vegetables evenly.
- Pour in the diced tomatoes (with their juices) and vegetable broth.

NUTRITIONAL FACTS (PER SERVING)

- **Serving Size:** 1 cup
- Calories: 46 kcal
- Total Fat: 0.3g
- Saturated Fat: 0g
- Cholesterol: 0mg
- Sodium: 2mg
- Carbohydrates: 11.5g
- Dietary Fiber: 1g
- Sugars: 8.6g
- Protein: 0.9g

DIRECTIONS

- Bring the mixture to a simmer.
- Once simmering, add the drained and rinsed chickpeas to the pot. Stir well to combine.
- Reduce the heat to low and let the stew simmer for 15-20 minutes, or until the vegetables are tender and the flavors have melded together.
- Season the stew with salt and pepper to taste.
- Serve the stew hot, garnished with fresh parsley or cilantro if desired.

ROASTED VEGETABLE MEDLEY

 Prep Time
15 Mins

Cook Time
30 Mins

 **Yields**
4 Servings

INGREDIENTS

- 1 medium zucchini, sliced
- 1 medium yellow squash, sliced
- 1 red bell pepper, sliced
- 1 yellow bell pepper, sliced
- 1 red onion, sliced
- 1 cup cherry tomatoes
- 2 cloves garlic, minced
- 2 tablespoons balsamic vinegar
- 2 tablespoons olive oil
- Salt and pepper to taste
- Fresh herbs (optional), such as rosemary or thyme.

DIRECTIONS

- Preheat your oven to 400°F (200°C).
- In a large bowl, combine all the sliced vegetables and minced garlic.
- Drizzle the balsamic vinegar and olive oil over the vegetables. Season with salt and pepper, and toss until the vegetables are evenly coated.
- Spread the vegetables out in a single layer on a large baking sheet.
- Roast in the preheated oven for 25-30 minutes, or until the vegetables are tender and starting to brown, stirring halfway through.
- Once roasted, remove from the oven and garnish with fresh herbs if desired.

NUTRITIONAL FACTS (PER SERVING)

- Calories: 160kcal
- Total Fat: 2g
- Saturated Fat: 0g
- Cholesterol: 0mg
- Sodium: 490mg
- Carbohydrates: 31g
- Dietary Fiber: 9g
- Sugars: 10g
- Protein: 8g

DIRECTIONS

- Serve hot as a side dish or over a bed of greens for a light meal.

VEGAN LENTIL CURRY

 Prep Time
10 Mins

Cook Time
30 Mins

 Yields
2 Servings

INGREDIENTS

- 1 cup dried green or brown lentils, rinsed and drained
- 1 small onion, finely chopped
- 2 cloves garlic, minced
- 1 small sweet potato, peeled and diced
- 1 cup diced tomatoes (fresh or canned)
- 1 cup vegetable broth
- 1 tablespoon curry powder
- 1 teaspoon ground cumin
- 1 teaspoon ground coriander
- 1/2 teaspoon turmeric
- Salt and pepper to taste
- Fresh cilantro for garnish (optional)

DIRECTIONS

- In a medium-sized pot, heat a little water or vegetable broth over medium heat. Add the chopped onion and garlic and sauté until softened, about 5 minutes.
- Add the diced sweet potato, lentils, diced tomatoes, vegetable broth, curry powder, cumin, coriander, turmeric, salt, and pepper to the pot. Stir well to combine.
- Bring the mixture to a boil, then reduce the heat to low and let it simmer, covered, for about 25-30 minutes, or until the lentils and sweet potatoes are tender, stirring occasionally.

NUTRITIONAL FACTS (PER SERVING)

- Calories: 275kcal
- Total Fat: 1g
- Saturated Fat: 0g
- Cholesterol: 0mg
- Sodium: 400mg
- Carbohydrates: 53g
- Dietary Fiber: 18g
- Sugars: 9g
- Protein: 18g

DIRECTIONS

- Once the lentils and sweet potatoes are cooked through and the curry has thickened slightly, taste and adjust seasonings as needed.
- Serve the lentil curry hot, garnished with fresh cilantro if desired.

WATERMELON AND FETA SALAD

 Prep Time
10 Mins

Cook Time
0 Mins

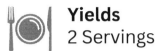 **Yields**
2 Servings

INGREDIENTS

- 2 cups cubed watermelon
- 50g feta cheese, crumbled
- 1/4 cup fresh mint leaves, chopped
- 1/2 small red onion, thinly sliced
- 1 tbsp balsamic glaze (optional)
- Salt and black pepper to taste

DIRECTIONS

- In a medium-sized mixing bowl, combine the cubed watermelon, crumbled feta cheese, chopped mint leaves, and thinly sliced red onion.
- Gently toss the ingredients until evenly mixed.
- Season the salad with salt and black pepper according to your taste preferences.
- Drizzle balsamic glaze over the salad if desired for extra flavor.
- Serve the salad immediately or chill in the refrigerator for 30 minutes before serving to enhance flavors.

NUTRITIONAL FACTS (PER SERVING)

- Calories: 105kcal
- Total Fat: 4g
- Saturated Fat: 2g
- Cholesterol: 13mg
- Sodium: 273mg
- Carbohydrates: 16g
- Dietary Fiber: 1g
- Sugars: 12g
- Protein: 4g

SPAGHETTI SQUASH WITH MARINARA SAUCE

 Prep Time
10 Mins

Cook Time
45 Mins

 Yields
2 Servings

INGREDIENTS

- 1 medium spaghetti squash
- 1 cup marinara sauce (look for a low-sugar or sugar-free option)
- 1 tablespoon olive oil
- Salt and pepper to taste
- Optional: grated Parmesan cheese and fresh basil for garnish

DIRECTIONS

- Preheat your oven to 400°F (200°C).
- Cut the spaghetti squash in half lengthwise and scoop out the seeds with a spoon.
- Brush the cut sides of the spaghetti squash with olive oil and season with salt and pepper.
- Place the spaghetti squash halves cut side down on a baking sheet lined with parchment paper or aluminum foil.

NUTRITIONAL FACTS (PER SERVING)

- Calories: 120kcal
- Total Fat: 4g
- Saturated Fat: 1g
- Cholesterol: 0mg
- Sodium: 390mg
- Carbohydrates: 20g
- Dietary Fiber: 5g
- Sugars: 8g
- Protein: 2g

DIRECTIONS

- Roast in the preheated oven for 35-45 minutes, or until the squash is tender and the flesh easily shreds into spaghetti-like strands with a fork.
- While the spaghetti squash is roasting, heat the marinara sauce in a saucepan over medium heat until warmed through.
- Once the spaghetti squash is cooked, use a fork to scrape the flesh into spaghetti-like strands.
- Divide the spaghetti squash between two plates and top with the warm marinara sauce.
- Garnish with grated Parmesan cheese and fresh basil if desired.

TUNA SALAD STUFFED IN LETTUCE WRAPS

 Prep Time
10 Mins

Cook Time
0 Mins

 Yields
2 Servings

INGREDIENTS

- 1 can (5 oz) of tuna in water, drained
- 1/4 cup diced cucumber
- 1/4 cup diced red bell pepper
- 2 tablespoons diced red onion
- 2 tablespoons fat-free Greek yogurt

DIRECTIONS

- In a mixing bowl, combine the drained tuna, diced cucumber, diced red bell pepper, diced red onion, and fat-free Greek yogurt.
- Mix until all ingredients are well combined.
- Spoon the tuna salad mixture into large lettuce leaves (such as romaine or iceberg lettuce) to create lettuce wraps.
- Serve immediately or refrigerate until ready to eat.

**NUTRITIONAL FACTS
(PER SERVING)**

- Calories: 70kcal
- Protein: 13g
- Fat: 0.5g
- Carbohydrates: 3g
- Fiber: 1g

MINESTRONE SOUP

Prep Time
15 Mins

Cook Time
30 Mins

Yields
2 Servings

INGREDIENTS

- 4 cups low-sodium vegetable broth
- 1 can (14.5 oz) diced tomatoes, undrained
- 1 small onion, diced
- 2 cloves garlic, minced
- 1 medium carrot, diced
- 1 celery stalk, diced
- 1/2 cup diced zucchini
- 1/2 cup diced green beans
- 1/2 cup small pasta (such as small shells or macaroni)
- 1 tsp dried oregano
- 1 tsp dried basil
- Salt and pepper to taste
- Optional: Parmesan cheese for garnis

DIRECTIONS

- In a large pot, heat the vegetable broth over medium heat.
- Add the diced tomatoes (with their juices) to the pot.
- Stir in the diced onion, minced garlic, diced carrot, diced celery, diced zucchini, and diced green beans.
- Add the dried oregano and dried basil to the pot, and season with salt and pepper to taste.
- Bring the soup to a simmer and let it cook for about 10 minutes, or until the vegetables start to soften.
- Stir in the small pasta and continue to simmer for another 10-12 minutes, or until the pasta is cooked al dente and the

NUTRITIONAL FACTS (PER SERVING)

- Calories: 120kcal
- Total Fat: 1g
- Saturated Fat: 0g
- Cholesterol: 0mg
- Sodium: 650mg
- Carbohydrates: 24g
- Dietary Fiber: 5g
- Sugars: 7g
- Protein: 5g

DIRECTIONS

- vegetables are tender.
- Taste the soup and adjust seasoning if necessary.
- Serve hot, garnished with Parmesan cheese if desired.

CHIA PUDDING

 Prep Time
5 Mins

Cook Time
0 Mins

 **Yields**
2 Servings

INGREDIENTS

- 1/4 cup chia seeds
- 1 cup plant-based milk (such as almond milk, coconut milk, or soy milk)
- 1 tablespoon maple syrup or agave syrup (optional, adjust to taste)
- Fresh fruits (such as berries, sliced banana, or mango) for topping.

DIRECTIONS

- **Mix Chia Seeds and Plant-Based Milk:** In a mixing bowl or jar, combine the chia seeds and plant-based milk. Stir well to combine.
- **Sweeten (Optional):** If desired, add maple syrup or agave syrup to sweeten the pudding. Stir again to distribute the sweetener evenly.
- **Let it Sit:** Cover the bowl or jar and refrigerate for at least 2 hours, or preferably overnight. This allows the chia seeds to absorb the liquid and form a pudding-like consistency.

NUTRITIONAL FACTS (PER SERVING)

- Calories: 150kcal
- Total Fat: 8g
- Saturated Fat: 1g
- Sodium: 80mg
- Carbohydrates: 16g
- Fiber: 9g
- Sugars: 5g
- Protein: 5g

DIRECTIONS

- **Serve:** Once the chia pudding has set, give it a good stir. If it's too thick, you can add a splash of plant-based milk to reach your desired consistency.
- **Top with Fresh Fruits:** Serve the chia pudding in bowls or glasses and top with your favorite fresh fruits.

BARRAMUNDI CEVICHE

 Prep Time
15 Mins

Cook Time
0 Mins

 Yields
2 Servings

Marinating Time: 30 Mins

INGREDIENTS

- 2 barramundi fillets, skin removed and diced into small cubes
- 1/2 red onion, finely diced
- 1 tomato, diced
- 1/2 cucumber, diced
- 1 jalapeño pepper, seeded and finely chopped (optional)
- 1/4 cup fresh cilantro, chopped
- Juice of 2-3 limes
- Salt and pepper to taste
- Tortilla chips or lettuce leaves for serving (optional)

DIRECTIONS

- In a medium-sized bowl, combine the diced barramundi, red onion, tomato, cucumber, jalapeño (if using), and cilantro.
- Squeeze the lime juice over the mixture until everything is well coated. Season with salt and pepper to taste.
- Cover the bowl with plastic wrap and refrigerate for at least 30 minutes to allow the flavors to meld together and the fish to "cook" in the acidic lime juice. You'll know it's ready when the fish turns opaque.
- Once ready, give the ceviche a final stir and adjust seasoning if necessary.

48

NUTRITIONAL FACTS (PER SERVING)

- Calories: 120kcal
- Total Fat: 1g
- Saturated Fat: 0g
- Cholesterol: 50mg
- Sodium: 40mg
- Carbohydrates: 7g
- Dietary Fiber: 2g
- Sugars: 3g
- Protein: 22g

DIRECTIONS

- Serve the barramundi ceviche chilled, either on its own or with tortilla chips or lettuce leaves for scooping.

BUFFALO CAULIFLOWER BITES

 Prep Time
10 Mins

Cook Time
25 Mins

 Yields
2 Servings

INGREDIENTS

- 1 small head of cauliflower, cut into florets
- 1/4 cup hot sauce (such as Frank's RedHot)
- 1 tbsp olive oil
- 1/2 tsp garlic powder
- 1/2 tsp onion powder
- Salt and pepper, to taste
- Ranch or blue cheese dressing for dipping (optional)

DIRECTIONS

- Preheat your oven to 450°F (230°C). Line a baking sheet with parchment paper or lightly grease it.
- In a large mixing bowl, combine the hot sauce, olive oil, garlic powder, onion powder, salt, and pepper.
- Add the cauliflower florets to the bowl and toss until they are evenly coated with the buffalo sauce mixture.
- Spread the cauliflower florets in a single layer on the prepared baking sheet.
- Bake in the preheated oven for 20-25 minutes, or until the cauliflower is tender and golden brown, stirring halfway through.

NUTRITIONAL FACTS (PER SERVING)

- Calories: 70kcal
- Total Fat: 4g
- Saturated Fat: 1g
- Cholesterol: 0mg
- Sodium: 620mg
- Carbohydrates: 7g
- Dietary Fiber: 3g
- Sugars: 3g
- Protein: 3g

DIRECTIONS

- Once cooked, remove the cauliflower from the oven and let them cool slightly before serving.
- Optionally, serve with ranch or blue cheese dressing for dipping.

BAKED APPLES WITH CINNAMON

 Prep Time
10 Mins

Cook Time
30 Mins

 **Yields**
2 Servings

INGREDIENTS

- 2 medium-sized apples
- 1 teaspoon cinnamon
- 1/2 teaspoon nutmeg (optional)
- Cooking spray or butter (optional)

DIRECTIONS

1. Preheat your oven to 375°F (190°C).
2. Wash the apples and pat them dry. Remove the cores from the apples using a corer or a knife, leaving the bottoms intact.
3. Place the cored apples in a baking dish.
4. In a small bowl, mix together the cinnamon and nutmeg.
5. Sprinkle the cinnamon mixture evenly over the apples, making sure to coat them well.
6. If desired, lightly spray the apples with cooking spray or dot them with butter to help them brown and prevent sticking.
7. Bake the apples in the preheated oven for

NUTRITIONAL FACTS (PER SERVING)

- Calories: 80kcal
- Total Fat: 0.4g
- Saturated Fat: 0.1g
- Cholesterol: 0mg
- Sodium: 0mg
- Carbohydrates: 21g
- Dietary Fiber: 4g
- Sugars: 15g
- Protein: 0.4g

DIRECTIONS

- 25-30 minutes, or until they are tender and slightly golden on top.
- Remove the baked apples from the oven and let them cool slightly before serving.

TUNA AND WHITE BEAN SALAD

 Prep Time
10 Mins

Cook Time
0 Mins

 Yields
2 Servings

INGREDIENTS

- 1 can (5 oz) tuna in water, drained
- 1 can (15 oz) white beans (such as cannellini beans or navy beans), drained and rinsed
- 1/2 small red onion, finely chopped
- 1/2 cup cherry tomatoes, halved
- 1/4 cup chopped fresh parsley
- 1 tablespoon capers, drained
- 1 tablespoon olive oil
- 1 tablespoon lemon juice
- Salt and pepper to taste
- Optional: fresh lemon wedges for serving

DIRECTIONS

- In a medium-sized mixing bowl, combine the drained tuna, white beans, chopped red onion, halved cherry tomatoes, chopped parsley, and capers.
- Drizzle the olive oil and lemon juice over the salad ingredients.
- Season with salt and pepper according to your taste preferences.
- Gently toss all the ingredients together until well combined.
- Divide the salad between two serving plates.
- Optionally, serve with fresh lemon wedges on the side for an extra burst of flavor.

NUTRITIONAL FACTS (PER SERVING)

- Calories: 250kcal
- Total Fat: 8g
- Saturated Fat: 1g
- Cholesterol: 20mg
- Sodium: 290mg
- Carbohydrates: 26g
- Dietary Fiber: 7g
- Sugars: 2g
- Protein: 20g

STEAMED MUSSELS WITH WHITE WINE AND GARLIC

 Prep Time
10 Mins

Cook Time
10 Mins

 **Yields**
2 Servings

INGREDIENTS

- 1 lb fresh mussels, cleaned and debearded
- 2 cloves garlic, minced
- 1/2 cup dry white wine
- 1 tablespoon olive oil
- Salt and pepper to taste
- Fresh parsley, chopped (for garnish, optional)

DIRECTIONS

- Heat olive oil in a large pot over medium heat. Add minced garlic and sauté for about 1 minute until fragrant.
- Pour in the white wine and bring it to a simmer.
- Add the cleaned mussels to the pot and cover with a lid. Steam the mussels for 5-7 minutes, shaking the pot occasionally, until the mussels have opened.
- Discard any mussels that remain closed after cooking.
- Season the steamed mussels with salt and pepper to taste.
- Serve the mussels in bowls, garnished with chopped parsley if desired.

NUTRITIONAL FACTS
(PER SERVING)

- Calories: 150kcal
- Total Fat: 5g
- Saturated Fat: 1g
- Cholesterol: 35mg
- Sodium: 400mg
- Carbohydrates: 4g
- Dietary Fiber: 0g
- Sugars: 0g
- Protein: 14g

SALADE NIÇOISE

 Prep Time
15 Mins

Cook Time
10 Mins

 **Yields**
4 Servings

INGREDIENTS

- 2 (5 oz) cans of water-packed tuna, drained
- 4 cups mixed salad greens
- 1 cup cherry tomatoes, halved
- 1/2 cup green beans, blanched and halved
- 2 hard-boiled eggs, sliced
- 1/4 cup black olives, pitted
- 2 tbsp capers
- 1/4 red onion, thinly sliced
- Salt and pepper to taste
- Optional: lemon wedges for serving

For the dressing:
- 2 tbsp red wine vinegar
- 1 tbsp Dijon mustard
- 2 tbsp extra virgin olive oil
- 1 garlic clove, minced
- Salt and pepper to taste

DIRECTIONS

- In a small bowl, whisk together the red wine vinegar, Dijon mustard, extra virgin olive oil, minced garlic, salt, and pepper to make the dressing. Set aside.
- Arrange the mixed salad greens on two plates.
- Divide the drained tuna, cherry tomatoes, blanched green beans, sliced hard-boiled eggs, black olives, capers, and red onion evenly between the two plates on top of the mixed greens.
- Drizzle the dressing over the salads.
- Season with additional salt and pepper to taste.
- Serve immediately, with optional lemon wedges on the side.

58

NUTRITIONAL FACTS (PER SERVING)

- Calories: 310kcal
- Total Fat: 15g
- Saturated Fat: 2.5g
- Cholesterol: 215mg
- Sodium: 550mg
- Carbohydrates: 10g
- Dietary Fiber: 4g
- Sugars: 4g
- Protein: 34g

SORGHUM SALAD

 Prep Time
10 Mins

Cook Time
50 Mins

 **Yields**
2 Servings

INGREDIENTS

- 1/2 cup sorghum grains
- 1 cup water or vegetable broth
- 1 cup cherry tomatoes, halved
- 1/2 cucumber, diced
- 1/4 red onion, finely chopped
- 1/4 cup fresh parsley, chopped
- 1 tablespoon lemon juice
- 1 tablespoon olive oil
- Salt and pepper to taste

DIRECTIONS

- Rinse the sorghum grains under cold water. In a medium saucepan, combine the sorghum grains and water or vegetable broth. Bring to a boil, then reduce heat to low, cover, and simmer for 45-50 minutes, or until the sorghum is tender and cooked through. Drain any excess liquid and let cool.
- In a large mixing bowl, combine the cooked sorghum grains, cherry tomatoes, cucumber, red onion, and parsley.
- In a small bowl, whisk together the lemon juice and olive oil. Season with salt and pepper to taste.

NUTRITIONAL FACTS (PER SERVING)

- Calories: 250kcal
- Total Fat: 7g
- Saturated Fat: 1g
- Cholesterol: 0mg
- Sodium: 10mg
- Carbohydrates: 45g
- Dietary Fiber: 8g
- Sugars: 5g
- Protein: 6g

DIRECTIONS

- Pour the dressing over the salad and toss until well combined.
- Serve the sorghum salad immediately, or refrigerate for later. Enjoy!

ZUCCHINI LASAGNA

 Prep Time
15 Mins

Cook Time
45 Mins

 **Yields**
2 Servings

INGREDIENTS

- 2 medium zucchinis
- 1 cup marinara sauce (look for a low-sugar or sugar-free option)
- 1 cup part-skim ricotta cheese
- 1 cup shredded part-skim mozzarella cheese
- 1 teaspoon dried oregano
- 1 teaspoon dried basil
- Salt and pepper to taste
- Cooking spray

DIRECTIONS

- Preheat your oven to 375°F (190°C).
- Slice the zucchinis lengthwise into thin strips, about 1/8 inch thick, using a mandoline or a sharp knife. These will serve as your lasagna noodles.
- In a small bowl, mix the ricotta cheese with dried oregano, dried basil, salt, and pepper until well combined.
- Spray a baking dish with cooking spray. Spread a thin layer of marinara sauce on the bottom of the dish.
- Place a layer of zucchini slices on top of the marinara sauce.
- Spread half of the seasoned ricotta

NUTRITIONAL FACTS (PER SERVING)

- Calories: 235kcal
- Total Fat: 11g
- Saturated Fat: 6g
- Cholesterol: 41mg
- Sodium: 478mg
- Carbohydrates: 13g
- Dietary Fiber: 3g
- Sugars: 7g
- Protein: 20g

DIRECTIONS

- cheese over the zucchini slices.
- Sprinkle half of the shredded mozzarella cheese over the ricotta layer.
- Repeat the layers - marinara sauce, zucchini slices, seasoned ricotta cheese, and shredded mozzarella cheese.
- Cover the baking dish with aluminum foil and bake in the preheated oven for 30 minutes.
- Remove the foil and bake for an additional 10-15 minutes, or until the cheese is melted and bubbly and the zucchini is tender.
- Let it cool for a few minutes before slicing and serving.

DANDELION GREENS SALAD

 Prep Time
10 Mins

Cook Time
0 Mins

 **Yields**
2 Servings

INGREDIENTS

- 4 cups fresh dandelion greens, washed and dried
- 1/4 cup cherry tomatoes, halved
- 1/4 cup cucumber, thinly sliced
- 1/4 cup red onion, thinly sliced
- 1/4 cup toasted walnuts, chopped
- 1/4 cup vegan feta cheese, crumbled (optional)
- Salt and pepper to taste

For the Dressing:
- 2 tablespoons extra virgin olive oil
- 1 tablespoon balsamic vinegar
- 1 teaspoon Dijon mustard
- 1 teaspoon maple syrup
- Salt and pepper to taste.

DIRECTIONS

- In a small bowl, whisk together the olive oil, balsamic vinegar, Dijon mustard, maple syrup, salt, and pepper to make the dressing. Set aside.
- In a large mixing bowl, combine the dandelion greens, cherry tomatoes, cucumber, red onion, and toasted walnuts. Toss to mix.
- Drizzle the dressing over the salad and toss until everything is evenly coated.
- If using, sprinkle the vegan feta cheese over the salad.
- Season with additional salt and pepper to taste, if desired.
- Serve immediately and enjoy!

NUTRITIONAL FACTS (PER SERVING)

- Calories: 180kcal
- Total Fat: 14g
- Sodium: 220mg
- Carbohydrates: 11g
- Dietary Fiber: 4g
- Sugars: 4g
- Protein: 4g

VEGEMITE AND AVOCADO TOAST

 Prep Time
5 Mins

Cook Time
5 Mins

 **Yields**
2 Servings

INGREDIENTS

- 2 slices of whole grain bread (choose a low-calorie option if available)
- 1 ripe avocado
- 2 teaspoons of Vegemite (adjust to taste)
- Salt and pepper to taste
- Optional toppings: sliced tomatoes, sprouts, or a sprinkle of nutritional yeast

DIRECTIONS

- Toast the slices of whole grain bread until they are golden brown and crispy.
- While the bread is toasting, cut the avocado in half, remove the pit, and scoop the flesh into a small bowl.
- Mash the avocado with a fork until it reaches your desired consistency. Add salt and pepper to taste.
- Once the toast is ready, spread half of the mashed avocado onto each slice.
- Spread 1 teaspoon of Vegemite onto each slice of toast, on top of the mashed avocado.
- Optional: Top with sliced tomatoes,

NUTRITIONAL FACTS (PER SERVING)

- Calories: 165kcal
- Total Fat: 9g
- Saturated Fat: 1g
- Cholesterol: 0mg
- Sodium: 306mg
- Carbohydrates: 18g
- Dietary Fiber: 6g
- Sugars: 1g
- Protein: 4g

DIRECTIONS

- sprouts, or a sprinkle of nutritional yeast for added flavor and nutrients.
- Serve immediately and enjoy!

PAVLOVA WITH FRESH BERRIES

 Prep Time
15 Mins

Cook Time
1 Hr 15 Mins

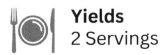 **Yields**
2 Servings

INGREDIENTS

- 2 egg whites
- 1/4 teaspoon cream of tartar
- 1/2 cup granulated sweetener (such as erythritol or Stevia)
- 1/2 teaspoon vanilla extract
- 1 cup mixed fresh berries (such as strawberries, blueberries, raspberries)
- Fresh mint leaves for garnish (optional)

DIRECTIONS

- Preheat your oven to 250°F (120°C). Line a baking sheet with parchment paper.
- In a clean, dry mixing bowl, beat the egg whites with an electric mixer on medium speed until foamy.
- Add the cream of tartar and continue to beat until soft peaks form.
- Gradually add the granulated sweetener, a little at a time, while continuing to beat on high speed. Beat until stiff, glossy peaks form.
- Gently fold in the vanilla extract.
- Spoon the meringue mixture onto the prepared baking sheet, forming two individual pavlova nests.

NUTRITIONAL FACTS (PER SERVING)

- Calories: 65kcal
- Total Fat: 0g
- Saturated Fat: 0g
- Cholesterol: 0mg
- Sodium: 64mg
- Carbohydrates: 14g
- Dietary Fiber: 2g
- Sugars: 9g
- Protein: 2g

DIRECTIONS

- Use the back of a spoon to create an indentation in the center of each nest, forming a well for the berries.
- Place the baking sheet in the preheated oven and bake for 1 hour and 15 minutes, or until the pavlovas are crisp on the outside and dry to the touch.
- Turn off the oven and leave the pavlovas inside to cool completely.
- Once cooled, carefully transfer the pavlovas to serving plates.
- Top each pavlova with an equal amount of fresh mixed berries.
- Garnish with fresh mint leaves if desired.

SUNFLOWER SHOOT SALAD

 Prep Time
10 Mins

Cook Time
15 Mins

 **Yields**
2 Servings

INGREDIENTS

- 2 cups sunflower shoots
- 1 cup cherry tomatoes, halved
- 1/2 cucumber, thinly sliced
- 1/4 red onion, thinly sliced
- 1/4 cup fresh parsley, chopped
- 1 tablespoon lemon juice
- 1 tablespoon extra virgin olive oil
- Salt and pepper to taste

DIRECTIONS

- Wash all the vegetables thoroughly. Slice the cherry tomatoes, cucumber, and red onion. Chop the fresh parsley.
- In a large mixing bowl, combine the sunflower shoots, cherry tomatoes, cucumber, red onion, and chopped parsley.
- In a small bowl, whisk together the lemon juice, extra virgin olive oil, salt, and pepper.
- Pour the dressing over the salad and gently toss until all the ingredients are well coated.
- Transfer the salad to serving plates or bowls and enjoy!

NUTRITIONAL FACTS
(PER SERVING)

- Calories: 70kcal
- Total Fat: 4.5g
- Saturated Fat: 0.5g
- Trans Fat: 0g
- Cholesterol: 0mg
- Sodium: 150mg
- Carbohydrates: 7g
- Dietary Fiber: 2g
- Sugars: 3g
- Protein: 2g

VEGGIE-PACKED PUMPKIN SOUP

 Prep Time
10 Mins

Cook Time
25 Mins

 **Yields**
2 Servings

INGREDIENTS

- 1 can (15 oz) pumpkin puree
- 1 small onion, chopped
- 2 cloves garlic, minced
- 2 cups vegetable broth
- 1 cup diced carrots
- 1 cup diced celery
- 1 tsp ground cumin
- 1/2 tsp ground cinnamon
- Salt and pepper to taste
- Fresh parsley or cilantro for garnish (optional)

DIRECTIONS

- In a large pot or Dutch oven, sauté the chopped onion and minced garlic over medium heat until softened, about 3-4 minutes.
- Add the diced carrots and celery to the pot, and cook for another 3-4 minutes until slightly tender.
- Stir in the pumpkin puree, vegetable broth, ground cumin, and ground cinnamon. Season with salt and pepper to taste.
- Bring the soup to a simmer, then reduce the heat to low. Cover and let the soup simmer for 15-20 minutes, stirring occasionally,

NUTRITIONAL FACTS (PER SERVING)

- Calories: 90kcal
- Total Fat: 0.5g
- Saturated Fat: 0g
- Cholesterol: 0mg
- Sodium: 610mg
- Carbohydrates: 20g
- Dietary Fiber: 6g
- Sugars: 9g
- Protein: 3g

DIRECTIONS

- until the vegetables are fully cooked and flavors are well combined.
- Once the soup is ready, use an immersion blender to blend the soup until smooth. Alternatively, you can transfer the soup in batches to a blender and blend until smooth, then return it to the pot.
- Taste the soup and adjust seasoning if needed.
- Serve the soup hot, garnished with fresh parsley or cilantro if desired.

Meal plan

for 30 Days

Date _____

	BREAKFAST	LUNCH	DINNER
MON	Overnight oats made with rolled oats, unsweetened almond milk, chia seeds, and mixed berries.	Quinoa salad with mixed greens, cherry tomatoes, cucumber, bell peppers, and a lemon-tahini dressing.	Baked tofu with roasted vegetables (such as broccoli, carrots, and cauliflower) and a side of steamed kale.
TUE	Smoothie made with spinach, banana, frozen berries, almond milk, and a tablespoon of flax seeds.	Lentil soup with carrots, celery, onions, and garlic.	Stuffed bell peppers with quinoa, black beans, corn, and salsa.
WED	Whole grain toast topped with mashed avocado and sliced tomato.	Chickpea salad with diced cucumber, bell peppers, red onion, and a lemon-tahini dressing.	Vegetable stir-fry with tofu, broccoli, bell peppers, snap peas, and a ginger-garlic sauce served over brown rice.
THU	Chia pudding made with unsweetened almond milk, chia seeds, and diced mango.	Spinach salad with strawberries, almonds, red onion, and a balsamic vinaigrette.	Baked sweet potato topped with black bean chili and diced avocado.
FRI	Smoothie bowl topped with sliced banana, granola, and shredded coconut.	Mediterranean quinoa salad with diced cucumber, cherry tomatoes, kalamata olives, and a lemon-tahini dressing.	Vegetable curry with chickpeas, cauliflower, carrots, and spinach served over quinoa.
SAT	Whole grain toast topped with almond butter and sliced banana.	Gazpacho soup with tomatoes, cucumbers, bell peppers, and onions.	Zucchini noodles (zoodles) with marinara sauce and roasted cherry tomatoes.

Meal plan
for 30 Days

Date
_____

	BREAKFAST	LUNCH	DINNER
SUN	Tofu scramble with diced bell peppers, onions, spinach, and turmeric.	Mixed bean salad with black beans, kidney beans, corn, cherry tomatoes, and a lime-cilantro dressing.	Buddha bowl with roasted sweet potatoes, chickpeas, broccoli, and tahini dressing.

Week 2-4

- Repeat this meal plan for days 8-14, or mix and match your favorite meals from the first week. Remember to drink plenty of water and adjust portion sizes according to your individual needs. Enjoy your plant-based journey!

ZERO POINT FOOD LIST

Zero Point Fruits

- Apples
- Apricots
- Bananas
- Blackberries
- Blueberries
- Cantaloupe
- Cherries
- Clementine
- Coconut
- Cranberries
- Dates
- Dragon Fruit
- Figs
- Grapefruit
- Grapes (any variety)
- Guava
- Honeydew Melon
- Jackfruit
- Kiwi
- Lemon
- Lime
- Mango
- Oranges
- Passion Fruit
- Peach
- Pears
- Pineapple

BEANS & LEGUMES

- Adzuki beans
- Alfalfa sprouts
- Bean sprouts
- Black beans
- Black-eyed peas
- Cannellini beans
- Chickpeas
- Edamame
- Fava beans
- Great Northern beans
- Hominy
- Kidney beans
- Lentils
- Lima beans
- Lupini beans
- Navy beans
- Pinto beans
- Refried beans, canned, fat-free
- Soy beans

CHICKEN & TURKEY BREAST

- Ground chicken breast
- Ground turkey, 98% fat-free
- Ground turkey breast
- Skinless chicken breast
- Skinless turkey breast

EGGS

- Egg substitute
- Egg whites
- Egg yolks
- Eggs

Zero Point Vegetables (Starchy & Non-Starchy)

- Arrowroot, raw
- Artichoke
- Arugula
- Asparagus
- Broccoli
- Beans (black, adzuki, cannellini, garbanzo, kidney, great northern, lima, pinto, etc.)
- Beans, refried (canned, fat-free, no added sugar)
- Green Beans
- Bok Choy
- Brussel Sprouts
- Cabbage
- Carrots
- Cauliflower
- Celery
- Chard
- Chickpeas
- Collards
- Corn
- Cucumber
- Daikon
- Edamame
- Eggplant
- Endive
- Fennel
- Ginger Root
- Kale
- Leeks
- Lettuce (any variety)
- Mushrooms
- Okra
- Peas
- Peppers (bell)
- Pickles (without sugar)
- Pumpkin
- Radishes
- Scallions (green onions)
- Spinach
- Sprouts
- Squash
- Tomatoes
- Turnips
- Zucchini

Zero Point Herbs and Spices

- Basil
- Chives
- Cinnamon
- Dill Weed
- Garlic
- Garlic Salt
- Italian Seasoning
- Oregano
- Paprika
- Parsley
- Pepper
- Peppermint
- Pumpkin Spice
- Rosemary
- Sage
- Salt
- Thyme

Zero Point Meat, Seafood and Poultry

- Calamari, grilled
- Chicken Breast (boneless, skinless)
- Crab (Alasaka king, Dungeness, queen, king)
- Crayfish
- Eggs

- Bass Fish
- Bluefish
- Carp
- Catfish
- Cod
- Eel
- Grouper
- Haddock
- Halibut
- Lobster
- Mackerel Fish
- Mussels
- Octopus
- Oysters
- Salmon (Atlantic and farm raised)
- Sardines
- Sea Bass
- Shrimp
- Sturgeon Fish
- Swordfish
- Tilapia Fish

FISH/SHELLFISH

- Abalone
- Alaskan king crab
- Anchovies, in water
- Arctic char
- Bluefish
- Branzino
- Butterfish
- Canned tuna, in water
- Carp
- Catfish
- Caviar
- Clams
- Cod
- Crabmeat, lump
- Crayfish
- Cuttlefish
- Dungeness crab
- Eel
- Fish roe
- Flounder
- Grouper
- Haddock
- Halibut
- Herring
- Lobster
- Mahi mahi
- Monkfish
- Mussels
- Octopus
- Orange roughy
- Oysters
- Perch
- Pike
- Pollock
- Pompano
- Salmon
- Sardines, canned in water or sauce
- Sashimi
- Scallops
- Sea bass
- Sea cucumber
- Sea urchin
- Shrimp
- Smelt
- Smoked haddock
- Smoked salmon
- Smoked sturgeon
- Smoked trout
- Smoked whitefish
- Snails
- Snapper
- Sole
- Squid

Zero Point Drinks

- Water
- Coffee, black (without sugar)
- Coke Zero (all varieties)
- Diet Coke (all varieties)
- Fresca (all varieties)
- Gatorade Zero
- Sparkling Ice Water (all flavors)
- Tea, black
- Vitamin Water Zero

Zero Point Snacks

- Applesauce, unsweetened
- Fruit cup (canned in water pack, no sugar added)
- Fruit cup (fresh)
- Vegetable Sticks
- Yogurt (greek, plain, fat-free, unsweetened)

IMPORTANT NOTICE!!!

We chose to make costs low so it can be accessible to everyone who would love to lose weight. As a result, we didn't include pictures for each recipes.

Please, reach out to us at popoolaadenike805@gmail.com if you would like to receive the pictures for each recipes.

HAPPY COOKING!

Made in the USA
Las Vegas, NV
09 March 2024

86953675R00046